ROSES AND CAVALIERS

An exciting historical adventure

in the

Tudor and Stuart times

by Michael Thomson

Illustrated by Bryony Jacklin

to my own Rose

Roses and Cavaliers
LD 702
ISBN 1 85503 163 9
© Text Michael Thomson
© Illustrations Bryony Jacklin
All rights reserved
First published 1993

LDA, Duke Street, Wisbech, Cambs PE13 2AE,
England

READ THIS FIRST!

You are the star in this adventure story. You begin in the year 2167, when Time Machines were invented. You are in the Time Patrol which looks after Time and makes sure that History isn't changed. Evil enemies of the Future like Thomas are travelling through Time to try to change History. If they succeed, they will be able to rule the world. Your job is to stop them.

You will need a copy of the Adventure Sheet at the back of this book. (You can write in this book if it is your book. If not, ask someone to photocopy the Adventure Sheet for you.) You also need two dice and a pencil.

As you travel through Time in this adventure you will meet many people and find out about the times they live in. You will also meet many enemies of the Future. You will have to fight them. When you fight you will throw your dice and work out your fighting skills. The story will tell you when to fight.

Look at the Adventure Sheet. It lists all the enemies you may have to fight. Every time you fight someone remember to fill in your Adventure Sheet. This is how you do it:

> Every time the story tells you to prepare for battle, you need to throw the two dice. Write the number of the dice throw in the Adventure Sheet in the 'Dice throw' column alongside the name of the enemy. Then add the dice throw to the number in the column called 'Your Skill points'. This number is your total Fighting Skill points. Write this number in the column called 'Your total Fighting Skill points'. The story gives you the enemy's Fighting Skill points. Write this number in the column called 'Enemy's Fighting Skill points'. You win the battle if you have the same as or more Fighting Skill points than the enemy. You lose if you have fewer Fighting Skill points than the enemy.

The Adventure Sheet also shows you that you have 25 Life Points. You may lose Life Points in the adventure. You may also be given some. Be careful, if you lose all your Life Points you die!

At the back of the book is another important part of your adventure – your Equipment List. You can also get this photocopied if you need to. In your adventure you will find or be given things that will help you. You must write them down on your Equipment List. Write down the story number you are on as well so you can find it again when you need it. If you do not have the right equipment you will have to go back to find it.

To begin the adventure start at the story number with **1** at the top. You will be told what to do next at the end of the story number. Now read on.

GOOD LUCK!

1

Crash! A screech of metal on stone rings out. You try to get control of your Time Machine. As you twist the wheel, the Time Machine scrapes along the wall of the landing bay at Time Patrol Centre. At last you get the craft under control. As the Machine comes to rest, you get out. The Time Machine looks a bit like a car without wheels. It has a cockpit like an aircraft. At the moment, there is a long gash of bent metal down one side. 'Well, what have you done this time?' a voice says behind you. You turn with a sheepish look on your face. It is Time Leader. 'Is there any reason why I should not take the cost of mending the Time Machine out of your wages?' she goes on.

You gulp and explain that the clock inside the Machine had broken. You had to use a candle-clock from King Alfred's time to set the coordinates to return (see *The Long Ship Invaders*).

Time Leader snorts. 'A likely story,' she says. 'Your next job had better be well done. Come on, I have a task for you.' You follow Time Leader to the control room. You are a member of the Time Patrol. It is the year 2167 and Time Travel has been invented. Your job is to stop a group, called the Time Destroyers, from changing History. If they change History, things might be very different. The Time Destroyers want to change things so that they can control the world. Yet no-one knows what the effect of changing History might be. It is better not to meddle! Imagine if your grandmother had been killed before your parents were born. Imagine if modern weapons had been used in the First World War. There are many changes that could have huge effects as the years go on.

Now go to **2**.

2

When you get to the control room Time Leader asks you to sit down. 'We have heard some grave news,' she begins. 'The Time Destroyers are active again. It seems that Time Destroyers are working in the Tudor and Stuart period.' She shows you a map of the Time Lines.

'We do not know very much. What we do know is that they are trying to stir up trouble with the Barons in the reign of King Henry the Seventh, the first Tudor monarch. We would like you to go and find out what is going on. You will also need to check out the Nexus Points of the whole period. Go to it!'

As you leave the room, you wonder if Time Patrol Leader ever lets up! You can now go to the Computer and check out the Nexus Points at **51**, find out about the Tudors and Stuarts in the library at **23** or go back to the Time Machine and start – go to **82**.

3

This is not what happened! Lose one Life Point and go to **25**. (Check your Event Chart at **50** if you want!)

4

You leap at him, blade forward. He moves to one side. He kicks you as you go past. You turn sharply and lunge again. The highwayman is a little careless. He moves too slowly and your sword grazes his arm. A small drop of blood shows that you have won! The highwayman bows and mounts up. He rides off without another word. Add 2 points to your Life Points.

One of your fellow travellers comes over to you. It is a woman with many veils over her face. 'Well done!' she says. 'Here, take this ring as a reward.' Now go to **73**.

5

Philip and Elizabeth did *not* marry. That would change History which is what the Time Destroyers want. Lose 1 Life Point and advise again at **127**.

6

Henry does not want to put the country into war again. Choose again at **76**.

Early in 1660, General Monk took London and the army was in control. He did not want to be involved in governing the country. You advise Parliament to recall Prince Charles. He promises to share power with Parliament and let people practise their own religion. In May 1660 he landed at Dover. He rode into London with crowds cheering him. The monarchy had been restored. The period that followed was known as the Restoration. Prince Charles became Charles II.

You go a few years forward in time. The Stuarts were sometimes known as Cavaliers. This came from the French *chevalier.* One of the meanings of chevalier was a gallant or noble person!

You can dress as a Stuart Gentleman (go to **84**) or Lady (go to **85**).

You go to look for Thomas at the theatre. People were fond of watching plays in those days. They used inn-yards for play-acting as actors often travelled about. Now you see that a theatre has been built. It has three rows of balconies around a courtyard. These are covered by a roof. The courtyard or 'pit' is open to the sky.

You hear a trumpet sound! The play is about to start. You forget all about Thomas the Time Destroyer. Perhaps you will see a play by William Shakespeare. You take out a book from your purse. (Both men and women had purses.) It is *The Complete Works of Shakespeare*. It is in very small print. The play starts. It is not a Shakespeare play. These were first put on around 1589 and then on into James I's reign (1603). You are a few years earlier!

Some of the actors are performing a dance. The women's parts are played by boys. The people watching are rather rowdy. Some take no notice, playing dice and cards. Others call for ale and nuts. Some even call out to the actors or throw things. A few young men are at the foot of the stage. They join in the dance. You find yourself dragged along. They are not very pleased at your dancing. They insist on teaching you the steps! (They have had a little too much ale, but still prove good teachers!) Write down *Elizabethan Dance Steps* on your Equipment List.

After the play you meet some of the actors. One is William Shakespeare. He was an actor before becoming a playwright. Just as you are about to talk to him you see Thomas! He has a knife! He is trying to stab Shakespeare. If he kills Shakespeare, History will be changed. One of the most important figures in English literature will die too early. Plays such as *Hamlet, Henry V, The Tempest* and many more will be lost forever! Quickly you grab Thomas's arm. He breaks free and runs off. Go to **9**.

You lose Thomas in the crowd! You go back and find that the actors have gone. Then you notice that your book, *The Complete Works of Shakespeare* is missing! You remember that someone once said that Shakespeare wrote with 'narry a blot'. That is with no mistakes in his writing. Not much was known about him. He couldn't have found your book, could he? He might have copied all the plays out over the years. No, that surely did not happen! The book is just lost. Surely the book from the future could not create the plays from the past? Oh well, you think to yourself, History is still right. The plays *were* published later. It doesn't matter if Shakespeare wrote them in the past or if there was some kind of time loop. They still exist. (Only you hope Time Leader doesn't find out about the missing book!)

You decide to go on in search of Thomas. Go to **49** and choose again.

10

You have wisely moved out of London. So have many other people. You go back to your Time Machine and go forward to 1666. You return to London on the night of 1st September. You are passing a baker's shop in Pudding Lane, east of London Bridge. You see a flare of light. A gush of flame bursts from the shop. You think that you see a figure dart from the shop. It looks like Thomas, the Time Destroyer!

Before you can get much closer the flames are fanned by the high wind of that hot summer. The flames are too high to get near now. What will you do? You can tell the night watchman – go to **17**, call the 999 – go to **27** or try and blow up the houses around the fire so that it cannot spread – go to **30**.

11

Well, you have chosen a Henry, but it is the wrong one! You have chosen Henry VIII not Henry VII! Choose 1485 (at **94**) or 1702 (at **34**).

12

If you chose to be a man you wear a plain, dark tunic and breeches. You have a black collar around the neck.

If you chose to be a woman you wear a plain, dark dress. You have a white apron, with a white collar around the neck. A white bonnet covers your head. Now go to **16**.

13

Thomas shakes off your grip. He slashes at you with a bit of rope. You duck and charge into him. You are both carried to the edge of the deck. The sea seems to boil beneath you as you lurch about on the deck. At last you hold him and other sailors come to your call. Thomas is chained up. The others think that he has been sent mad by drinking too much sea water!

At last the sails are trimmed. The ship is safe and can ride out the storm. Now you need to know where you are! Do you have the Latitude and Longitude Chart? If you do, go to **14**. If you do not, go back to **42**.

14

Have a look at the map and the Chart (**15**). You can see two marks on the sea. One is an X, the other Y. The X is west of Africa and the Y is east of Africa (the Y is around the Cape of Good Hope on towards India and the Eastern trade places). These Latitude and Longitude numbers show the two points.

(i) 15° East 30° South (ii) 60° East 15° South

You will need to read the Chart carefully at **15** to help you. The chart will explain what the numbers mean. Which set of numbers shows a point to the **east** of Africa?

If you think (i) shows a point to the east, go to **29**. If you think (ii) shows a point to the east, go to **64**.

LATITUDE AND LONGITUDE CHART

There are no landmarks at sea. To try and pinpoint a place, sailors use lines of Longitude and Latitude. These are like coordinates. A make-believe set of grids is placed over the Earth. The grid lines running North-South we call lines of Longitude. The grid lines running East-West are lines of Latitude. You can use the lines to find any place on the Earth.

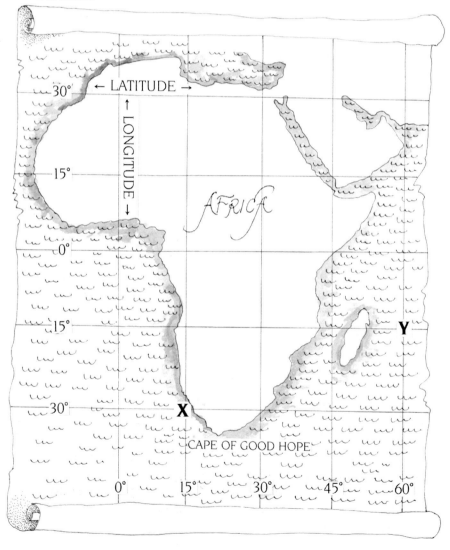

The map opposite shows where you are sailing with Vasco da Gama. It shows the Latitude and Longitude lines for this part of the world.

The lines 50° East and 10° South give a point just to the north of the island of Madagascar. 'East' means east of the 0° Longitude line. 'South' means south of the 0° Latitude line (the Equator).

So 50° East is on the line 50° east of the 0° line of Longitude. 10° South is on a line 10° south of the 0° line of Latitude. Where the two lines cross is the point!

Use the map to answer the question in paragraph 14. You can get some help from an adult if you need to. Your Geography teacher is a good bet!

16

You join a group at one of their prayer meetings. You will have to be careful what you say. The Puritans felt that bright clothes were wicked and curled hair was a sign of vanity. They did not use a prayer book but had a very simple form of worship. Hard work and modesty were very important. Theatre, drinking and displays of merry-making were all frowned upon.

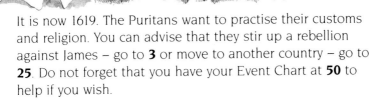

It is now 1619. The Puritans want to practise their customs and religion. You can advise that they stir up a rebellion against James – go to **3** or move to another country – go to **25**. Do not forget that you have your Event Chart at **50** to help if you wish.

17

You run to call the night watchman. He went round the streets in those days. The night watchman calls out the watermen. The London watermen were the first firemen. They had pumps, tanks and buckets. You form part of a human chain. You pass buckets of water from the river, along the chain to the fire.

All the houses are made of wood. They are also very near each other in the narrow streets. It is too late to stop the fire which is spreading quickly. You can try house clearing – go to **30**, or if you have tried that, go to **41**.

18

This was a bit tricky. Henry is trying to bring law and order back to the country. He does not want any more fighting. The two roses are put together to make the Tudor Rose, like this:

The Rose has become a symbol for Tudor times.

Now you dress as a servant. You can wear a shirt, loose breeches and leggings or a dress, apron and white wool cap.

You decide that your English will get you by. You use a country accent. One of the things you read before you came was that there is a great range of accents and dialects in these times. In fact Elizabeth I, in later years, was to remark that she could hardly understand Francis Drake as his accent was so thick!

You hang around the court of Henry VII, pretending to be a servant. Then you see some well-dressed men talking together. They look like nobles. You know one! It is Nardek, your old enemy from Saxon times (see *The Long Ship Invaders*). You hide behind a curtain and listen.

It seems that Nardek is now known as Thomas Wright. He has been behind a plot to put the House of York back on the throne. The plot involves men called Lambert Simnel and Perkin Warbeck. They were defeated by Henry. Now Wright is trying to get the nobles to rebel. You can try and get Henry to make war on the Barons – go to **6** or find a way to enforce the law and make the nobles obey him – go to **76**.

You decide to be a Parliamentarian. Parliament holds London and Charles marches south to London. The two armies met at Edgehill, near Warwick. Prince Rupert, the King's nephew makes a dashing cavalry charge. You see Thomas laying about with his sword as they chase the Parliamentarians. Then a counter-attack is launched. The Earl of Essex leads a charge toward the King. Many of his bodyguards are killed and the King is nearly captured. In the end no side can claim victory. Oliver Cromwell, the MP for Cambridge, is watching the battle. He decides to train a better army. You can go and help him train his men – go to **24** or you can fight another battle at once – go to **105**.

20

Oliver Cromwell, with your help, trains his men to be a strong fighting force. Many of his men were Puritans, often called Roundheads because of their close-cropped hair.

Cromwell's army was later called the New Model Army. It was the first regular British army. The men were well-equipped. Marching and line formation takes up a large part of their training. This is so the army can reform quickly when the lines are broken. The men are taught to charge hard. Rules were strict – no drunkenness or swearing. The men were also well-paid.

Now things are reaching a head. The Scots agree to help the Parliamentarians. The Battle of Marston Moor in 1644 is a defeat for the Royalists. The Scots and Parliamentarians outnumber them. In 1645 you prepare for the Battle of Naseby, in Leicestershire. Do you have your New Model Army Uniform? Check your Equipment List. If you do, go to **35**. If you do not, go back to **24**.

21

A lot has happened since the Fire. Charles II died in 1685.
James II came to the throne. Once again religion was to play
a part in affairs of state. James was a Roman Catholic. When
a group of Protestants rebelled he sent many to their death
for treason. This was at court trials known as 'The Bloody
Assizes'. After only three years people in England sent for
Mary and her husband William of Orange to come and rule.
They lived in Holland and were asked to invade. James fled to
France and Mary and William were made joint rulers in 1689.

Now James has landed in Ireland, with a French army. He has
called on Catholic Ireland to support him. More seeds of the
Northern Ireland troubles of the future are sown. James's
army surrounds the Protestant stronghold in Londonderry (or
Derry as it had been known). 15,000 men, women and
children starve to death. Then William lands and James is
defeated in the Battle of the Boyne. After that the Catholics'
land around the north of Ulster was given to the English and
the Scots as a reward for their service to William of Orange.
They became known as Orangemen. You wish that there was
some way to prevent all this bitterness. You must go on to
the court of William and Mary. Check your Equipment List.
Do you have the Signet Ring? If you do, go to **32**. If you do
not, you will have to go back to **4**.

22

You decide to join Francis Drake (later Sir Francis). You could
have joined some other Elizabethan seamen. Sir Walter
Raleigh went to Virginia in America. He took tobacco and
potatoes back to England. Also John Hawkins was a well-
known slave trader. He would capture people in Africa and
sell them as slaves to work on the mines and plantations of
the Americas. You vow to help stop this vile slave trade. You
will come back in time to do this. (Another book in the series
tells how you do this.)

Both John Hawkins and Francis Drake vowed revenge on the
Spanish when they were attacked in Mexico. They became
almost like pirates against the Spanish.

Now you join the *Pelican* in 1577 (Drake renamed it the
Golden Hind later). He was starting a secret mission to sail
around the world. You board dressed as a *cooper*, the person
who looked after the ship's stores. Just then you see Thomas
on the deck. He sees you and runs off! He will try and stop
the *Golden Hind* leaving. You run after him. Where will you
look? Look carefully at the picture of the *Pelican (Golden
Hind)*.

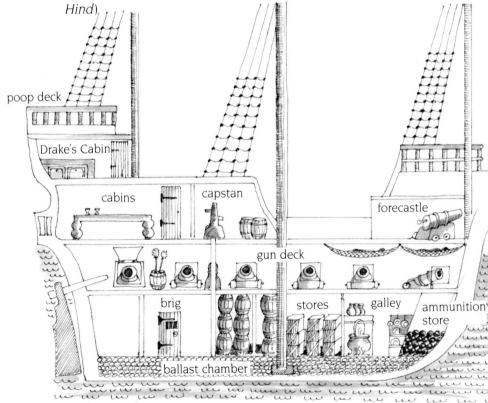

Write down where you think Thomas went here

. . . .

Now turn to **31**.

As you walk to the library you find a bit of paper in your pocket. It is a part of a Chart you had from another Time Visit you made (*The Longship Invaders*). It lists some of the Roman numerals and our number system. This could be useful in working out who the Kings and Queens are.

When you get to the library you jot down some notes on it. This is what you now have.

Roman Numerals	Modern Numbers	
I	1	These numbers are used for kings and queens so that Richard III is Richard the Third and Henry VII is Henry the seventh and so on.
II	2	
III	3	
IV	4	
V	5	
VI	6	
VII	7	
VIII	8	

Write down *Numeral Notes* on your Equipment List.

Then you go to the books in the library. After a lot of reading and typing into the Computer you print out an Event Chart. Write down *Event Chart* on your Equipment List. You can see this at **50** when you want. Do not forget to make a note of the number that you are on so that you can go back.

Now you can go to see the Event Chart at **50**, go to the Computer at **51**, or go to the Time Machine Bay at **67**.

You go to help Cromwell train his men. This is useful as better troops were needed. You are given a uniform. Write down *New Model Army Uniform* on your Equipment List. Now go to **20**.

25

You say, quietly, that it would be good to have a new land where you can develop as you want. This is an idea that finds favour. In 1620 the 'Pilgrim Fathers', as the group were known, set sail. They went in the *Mayflower* and landed in North America (at Cape Cod, Massachusetts). They called the area New England. Many more Puritans were to go and live in America. Their way of life had an important part to play in areas of North America.

Now you will have to go on to the Nexus Point. If you check **51** you will see that this is to do with Civil War. Go to **52**.

26

You decide to make sure that Christopher Columbus makes his voyage. Columbus was an Italian sailor who wanted to try a western route to the East. They must have known the world was round and wanted to get to the East around the world. Henry VII would not support a voyage, but the King and Queen of Spain did. He was given three ships, including the now famous *Santa Maria*.

In 1492 you find a place as a *younker* on the *Santa Maria*. A younker was a young sailor who climbed the mast to unfurl the great sails. You sail west. Sailing from Europe, you have to sail into the wind which comes from the west most of the time. This is the 'prevailing wind', and ships had to sail into these 'Westerlies'. This meant that ships had to 'tack' (go in a zig-zag course).

You spend a lot of time going up and down the mast taking the sails in and out!

After many days you are given the task of finding out the ship's speed. This will help Columbus work out where he is. How are you going to do this? You can look at how fast the clouds are going by and count how long they take – **44** or try and find a way to see how fast the ship is going along in the water – **56**.

27

What? Where are you going to find a telephone in 1666? Lose 2 Life Points and choose the night watchman – **17** or the house clearing – **30**.

28

It will be too dark to see where you are firing. Not a good idea! Go and choose again at **71**.

29

You have picked the X point. This is still to the west of Africa. You have not found the sea route. Lose one Life Point and go back to **14** and try again.

30

You try and tell some people who come up to the fire that they must destroy the house around the fire. This will keep the fire in one place. They take no notice at first. The fire rages and spreads, fanned by the wind. You can try telling the night watchman – go to **17** or, if you have tried that, go to **41**.

If you wrote The Galley (Thomas might poison the food), Drake's Cabin (he might kill Drake), The Gun Deck (he might try to blow up the ship) or the Ballast Chamber (he might try to hole the ship) add one point to your score.

Then you go to the room you wrote down. As you climb down a ladder you see Thomas again. He has fallen off the ship in his haste. He spits out the water of the harbour as he swims to shore. You see a Spanish-looking man help him out of the water. You are sure he will try something later. You had better go on the trip with Drake.

Life is not much fun on board. You and the other sailors are all cramped up in the forecastle. Some sling hammocks in the gun deck. In bad weather everything is wet. The smell of sweat, bilge-water and damp is awful!

The food is pretty poor. The bread and cheese is soon mouldy. Salted meat and fish are the main food. The fresh water is soon stale as well! Some of the ship's 'hare tack' or biscuits have worms in! After a few months some of the sailors have bleeding gums. They have flaky skin with bruises. The skin is sore and bleeds. Some complain of pain in the joints. The men come to you as cooper for some help. Will you put butter on the sores – go to **63** or give them some lime juice – go to **53**.

32

You go to the court of William and Mary. You see Thomas there. He is trying to tell the rulers to block what Parliament is trying to do. He tells William and Mary to take the army and rule on their own. He also tries to get John Churchill, the Commander of the Army to join James.

You show William and Mary the signet ring. It is the ring of one of their courtiers. She is now an old lady but recalls your help with the highwayman. People listen to your advice – go to **38**.

33

Coal was a fuel used more often in Tudor times. As it produces a lot of smoke, a hole in the roof is not enough. Try gas – **119** or long chimneys – **101**.

34

This date is over two hundred years too late! Lose 1 Life Point and choose 1509 (at **11**) or 1485 (at **94**).

35

You wear the uniform of Cromwell's 'Ironsides', a nickname given for their hard fighting. You wear an iron helmet and a brown leather coat. (The infantry wore scarlet tunics.) Your forces are better equipped than the Royalists. At first there is fierce fighting. You are on horseback. Out of the melée of cavalry, a Royalist appears. Sometimes called a Cavalier, he has long hair and a hat with a feather in it.

Then you see that the rider is Thomas. Throw your dice and prepare to meet:

THOMAS AS A STUART CAVALIER
FIGHTING SKILLS 16

If you win go to **43**, if you lose go to **75**.

36

You wear padded breeches with a doublet. You put on a pointed beard from the make-up wardrobe. You wear a ruff around your neck. You also pack some simpler clothes: a gown, breeches and a flat woollen cap. Now go to **49**.

37

You wear a tight bodice with padded sleeves. It is richly embroidered. You have an underskirt of patterned silk. You also pack some simpler clothes: a gown and Dutch cap. Now go to **49**.

38

You can draw up a list of ideas for reform – go to **106**, talk to John Churchill – go to **108**, deal with Thomas the Time Destroyer once and for all – go to **116** or go back to Time Patrol Headquarters – **128**.

39

You hear the whine of shot as it goes past your ear!
Now go to **40**.

As the smoke clears you see that Thomas has gone. Bits of
the musket are left. It blew up! (Guns sometimes did that in
those days. They also took over a minute to reload!) You see
a bit of paper on the ground. Thomas must have dropped it.
You pick it up. The paper is a guide to this Time that has
been given to Thomas by the Time Destroyers' Headquarters.
The title says 'Henry VIII's advisers and his wives'. Write
Henry's Advisers' and Wives' Scroll on your Equipment List.
You can see this any time at **45**. (Make a note of the number
you're on so you do not lose your place.)

Now you know that Henry will declare himself Head of the
Church of England. The effects of this will change History
down the years. There are also other reasons for the new
Church. For example many people did not want to pay taxes
to the Pope. Also new religious ideas were sprouting up.
Martin Luther in Germany had set up the Protestant Church
and its ideas were spreading into other parts of Europe.

You can now take the part of one of Henry VIII's main
advisers – go to **46**, one of Henry VIII's six wives – go to **47** or
try and find out where Thomas the Time Destroyer went – **48**.
(It might be helpful to look at the *Advisers' and Wives' Scroll*
before you choose!)

41

Over the next few days London burned. Samuel Pepys wrote:

*'All over the Thames, with one's face to the wind, you were
almost burned with a shower of fire-drops ... churches and
houses were on fire and flaming; and a horrid noise the
flames made, and the cracking of houses was their ruin.'*

On 4th September St. Paul's Cathedral burned. The flames melted the lead on the roof. The molten lead streamed down, burning and hot. As the flames neared the Tower of London, which was full of gunpowder, houses were cleared. Pepys' house was not burned. He had buried his special wine and cheese in his garden to keep it safe!

You have worked hard helping to put out the fire. At last it stops. You are covered in ash and grime. Nearly all of old London was burnt down. The later rebuilding was in stone, brick and tile. Streets were made wider.

You wonder if it was one of the Time Destroyers who set fire to that baker's shop. You stay on in this Time to see if you can find Thomas. You go into one of the coffee shops that were becoming popular.

You see a man looking over some plans for a building. You are told that it is Christopher Wren (later Sir Christopher). He was a well-known architect who rebuilt a lot of London. He is going to rebuild St. Paul's Cathedral. You sit next to him. You make a few comments! You can tell him to build the Cathedral like the old 14th century churches – go to **61** or to look at the domes of Italy for ideas – go to **129**.

Vasco da Gama was a well-known Portugese explorer. The Portugese were trying to find a sea route to the East. They thought that they could find a way south. They sailed further and further south along the west coast of Africa.

You set the Time Machine to go to 1497 to join Vasco da Gama as he explored. Before you go you take a chart with you. It shows lines of Latitude and Longitude. Write down *Latitude and Longitude Chart* on your Equipment List. You can look at this at **15**.

You manage to get onto a ship as a *swabber*. That is someone who cleans or 'swabs' the decks. Vasco da Gama took four ships with him. As you sail on down the west coast you get near to the bottom of southern Africa (the Cape of Good Hope as it is known now). A storm begins to brew up. The wind starts to whip the waves up into white froth. Dark clouds cover the sky. The rain sheets down and needles into your face. The ship is blown from one side to another. The sails will need to be trimmed (some sails taken down) or the ship will blow over. As the wind lashes you, Vasco da Gama calls for all hands to help. You hope that the storm will not sink the ship. (Now you know why it was called the Cape of Good Hope!)

Just then you see a figure that you know. It is Thomas Wright, the Time Destroyer. He is trying to cut the sails away and throw them overboard. Then the ship will be stranded in mid-ocean! Other Time Destroyers will come and pick him up once he has stranded the ship. You rush over and grab him. The rain drenches you as you struggle. Throw your dice and meet:

THOMAS: THE MAD SAILOR
FIGHTING SKILLS 10

If you win go to **13**. If you lose go to **121**.

43

Thomas's horse crashes into you and you nearly fall. You cross swords as you both cut and thrust with your rapiers. You duck as Thomas's sword swooshes over your head. Wheeling and turning, you try to gain the advantage. Thomas is also a good swordsman. You thank your lucky stars for all the swordplay practice you put in at Time Patrol.

As Thomas lunges forward you see a gap. With a twist of your wrist you plunge your sword into the flesh of his arm. Thomas drops the sword. He gallops off before you can do anything! You look about you. The Battle of Naseby is won!

Later Charles managed to escape and raise an army. But this was put down easily by the New Model Army at Preston in 1648.

Charles was put on trial. He was beheaded in 1649. Until the end he said that no-one had any right to try him. Cromwell said that execution was the only way to deal with Charles. The country was now ruled by Parliament – go to **59**.

44

This may tell you something about how fast the wind is blowing! It will not give you the speed of the ship. Choose again at **26**.

45

HENRY VIII: ADVICE ON ADVISERS AND WIVES

Being close to Henry VIII could be rather risky. Do not try to tell him what to do too! Also do not take the part of one of his wives! This is what happened to his advisers and wives.

ADVISERS	WIVES	Date of Marriage
Thomas Wolsey: Became rich and powerful but did not help Henry divorce Catherine. Disgraced – died just as he was about to be executed!	**Catherine of Aragon** divorced	1509
	Anne Boleyn beheaded for supposedly being unfaithful	1534
Thomas Cranmer: Helped Henry and drew up a Prayer Book for the Church of England. Then, when Mary came to the throne he was burnt!	**Jane Seymour** died after giving birth	1536
	Anne of Cleves divorced, sent away	1540
Thomas Cromwell: Helped Henry close the monasteries. Then Henry executed him for giving bad advice.	**Catherine Howard** beheaded for being unfaithful	1540
	Catherine Parr nursed him in old age	1543
Thomas More: A scholar: Henry wanted to start the Church of England but Thomas would not agree. He was executed as a traitor.		

46

You decide to become one of Henry's advisers. You end up being sent to the executioner! Well, you were warned! (see **45**). Lose 3 Life Points as you are rescued by the Time Patrol. They send you in search of Thomas the Time Destroyer. Go to **48**.

47

You decide to become one of Henry's wives. You end up being sent to the executioner! Well, you were warned! (see **45**). Lose 3 Life Points as you are rescued by the Time Patrol. They send you in search of Thomas the Time Destroyer. Go to **48**.

48

You set off after Thomas the Time Destroyer. He is nowhere to be seen. He has gone on into the reign of Edward VI. Edward was the son of Henry and Jane Seymour. He was never very healthy and died when he was sixteen. During his reign the Church of England developed further. Archbishop Cranmer had the Book of Common Prayer written in English, not Latin. You find that the Time Destroyer has gone on to the reign of Mary. He plans to make more trouble over the differences between Catholics and Protestants. Go to **65**.

49

Now you are ready to search the Elizabethan times for Thomas. You can:

Go and see a play at the theatre – **8**

Join Francis Drake on his ship the *Golden Hind* – **22**

Visit Elizabeth I's court – **117**

Search the town for him – **93**.

EVENT CHART

Events	Dates
Henry VII came to throne. Married Princess Elizabeth of York.	1485
Star Chamber to try nobles. Also Royal judges around country.	1487
Discoveries and voyages: Christopher Columbus finds West Indies.	1492
Vasco da Gama sailed past Cape of Good Hope.	1497/98
John Cabot finds Newfoundland.	1497
Amerigo Vespucci claims to be first European on American mainland.	1507 (book about his voyages)
Henry VIII on throne.	1509
Ferdinand Magellan sails around South America and becomes the first European to sail around the world.	1517–1521
James IV of Scotland defeated at Flodden.	1513
Cloth of Gold meeting with French.	1520
Pope's rule of Church removed, Church of England began with Henry VIII as its Head (also Act of Succession).	1534
Monasteries began to be closed ('Dissolution of Monasteries').	1539
Edward VI came to throne.	1547

More changes in Church. Book of Common Prayer.	1549
Mary Tudor ('Bloody Mary') on throne. Roman Catholic Church restarted.	1553
Elizabeth I on throne. Church of England restarted.	1558 1559
John Knox – Protestant Church in Scotland.	1559
More adventurers/explorers including Francis Drake around world in the *Golden Hind* and Walter Raleigh.	1577–1580
Writers such as William Shakespeare, Christopher Marlowe, Ben Johnson, Francis Bacon were around at this time.	
Spanish Armada.	1588
James I (James VI of Scotland) came to throne. First of Stuart monarchs.	1603
Gunpowder Plot.	1605
Mayflower sails and Pilgrims land in America.	1620
Charles I comes to throne. Tried to rule without Parliament.	1625
Civil War ('Roundheads v Cavaliers').	1642–1645 and 1648
Battles: Edgehill 1642 Marston Moor 1644 Naseby 1645	
Charles I executed.	1649

Cromwell's Protectorate (Commonwealth 1649–1650).	1653–1658
Charles II came to the throne.	1660
Great Plague.	1665
Fire of London. (Samuel Pepys.)	1666
James II came to throne. Many scientific developments eg. Gravity (Newton) Chemistry (Boyle) Circulation of blood (Harvey)	1685 During the 17th century (1600–1700)
William and Mary came to throne.	1689
Many new Laws and Rights passed (Bill of Rights, Habeas Corpus, Act of Settlement).	1689–1701
Anne came to throne (last of Stuarts).	1702
Battle of Blenheim.	1704
Act of Union (England and Scotland joined).	1707

Now you can go back to the number you were reading.

51

You head to the Computer. The Nexus Point of a time is an important event. There are many events of course, but some are more likely to be visited by the Time Destroyers. These are events that might change the future if they happen differently. The Time Patrol Computer tries to predict the Nexus Points that could be important.

You type in your request. You get this print out:

Nexus Points for Tudor and Stuart period

The break with the Roman Catholic Church and
    religious issues.
Explorations and Discoveries
The Spanish Armada
The Civil War and Cromwell's victories
The Bill of Rights and other Acts of Parliament

Write down *Nexus Points* on your Equipment List. Then go to
the library – **23** or the Time Machine bay – **67**.

52

You go on to the reign of Charles I. Charles, like James and
other rulers before him, said that they ruled by 'Divine Right'.
They said that God wanted them to be King and they could
rule as they liked. Parliament, however, wanted more power
and this was the beginning of the events that were to lead to
the Civil War.

The question was – should the King or Parliament rule? You
need to make sure History takes place as it should. You and
Thomas the Time Destroyer are members of Charles's court.
You can

(a) Advise Charles to rule without Parliament.
(b) Call Parliament to get them to agree on taxes.
(c) Extend the 'Ship Money' taxes without calling
    Parliament.
(d) Try to arrest Members of Parliament in the House
    of Commons.
(e) Agree to all that Parliament asks for.

If you chose a, c, or d, go to **124**. If you chose b or e, go
to **120**.

You have some limes. You took them on board for this very problem. The sailors have scurvy. This is due to lack of Vitamin C. Vitamin C comes from fresh fruit and vegetables. These were not taken to sea as they went bad so quickly. Limes have a lot of Vitamin C in them. They can be kept for a long time. You give the sailors a little juice every day. They soon get better. It is not until over 100 years later that the British Navy used limes all the time. Of course, it was much later that people understood about Vitamin C. The British were called 'limeys'. It is a name that some Americans still call the British. It is slang now, but in those days meant sailors who took limes to sea. For now you have helped some of the crew. Go to **54**.

54

At last you get to the Magellan Straits. This is the passage around South America. Drake's ship is the only one to go around the Straits. He renames the ship the *Golden Hind*. You are now in the Pacific Ocean.

One day there is a shout from the lookout. Sails have been seen. As you get closer you see that it is a large ship flying Spanish colours (the Spanish flag). It is a Spanish galleon!

Galleons have many guns, but are slow moving. Drake decides to board the ship. A few volleys of cannon fire are traded then Drake brings the *Golden Hind* up close. Grappling irons are thrown across. The crew (and you) swarm across with cutlasses, knives and clubs.

As you board the Spanish ship one of the sailors attacks with sword drawn! Throw your dice and prepare to meet:

SPANISH SAILOR
FIGHTING SKILLS 14

If you win go to **69**, if you lose go to **87**.

55

You tell Cranmer about the sea voyage of Christopher Columbus. He yawns. He has heard it all before! After all it was over thirty years ago. Better try again at **98**.

Right! You go and get a 'log-line'. This is a log tied to a long bit of rope. The log is thrown into the sea at the stern (back!) of the ship. The ship pulls the log along. You play out the rope as the log drags it off the deck. There are knots tied in the rope. The faster the ship is going, the more rope you have to play out. You can then work out how fast the ship is going in knots per hour. (Ship speed is still called 'knots' today.)

Just as you are about to count up the knots you see some pale marks on the rope. Some of the knots have been removed! Someone is trying to get you to work out the wrong speed. This could put Columbus off course. Quickly you tie some more knots in the correct place.

A few days after you see a twig and some driftwood floating in the sea. Land ahead! Columbus has found land to the west! He does not know that America is there. He thinks the world is smaller than it is. He calls the land the 'West Indies' because he thinks the land is part of the Indian and Indonesian Spice Islands! You try to tell him that it is a new land but he takes no notice. In fact the native people of this land (what later was called America) are still called 'Indians' because of this mistake. America was named after Amerigo Vespucci who wrote a book about his explorations in 1507.

The West Indies are tropical islands. You pick some coconuts as a reminder. Write *coconuts* on your Equipment List.

Now that Columbus has found land to the West which will lead to finding Central and South America you can go to Vasco da Gama – **42**, John Cabot – **72**, or Time Patrol Headquarters – **102**.

57

Your Time Machine has been hidden in the country outside London. You decide to take a stagecoach into London. You find one going into London at a nearby inn. The coach is drawn by horse and the ride is not much fun. You bump and crash along the muddy track. The coach gets stuck in a huge rut in the road. One of the people in the coach tells a story about a rut being so deep that someone drowned in the water in the bottom of it! You say that you can well believe it!

The coach is then stopped at a gate with spikes on it. It is a turnpike. A toll for the upkeep of the road has to be paid. You grumble about the fact that not much seems to have been spent on the road.

You tell the man next to you that they should have springs on the carriage. He looks puzzled. You talk to him about the way in which the coach slams down on the ground. You talk about ways in which heavy objects crash into others. The man stops talking. He gets out a notebook and writes down some figures. He looks thoughtful. He tells you his name is Isaac Newton. If it is the Newton that discovered the Law of Gravity, he would be about 23 years old now, in 1665. Newton published a major work in 1687 (*Principia Mathematica*). Perhaps it is this Newton and you have given him the seeds of an idea which his genius later understood. You wonder if Time Leader will be angry or pleased. Just as you are thinking on these matters, the coach rounds a corner. There, in a wooded part of the road, stands a highwayman! Go to **96**.

58

You put on a Red Rose. Quickly you see that you have made a mistake. Go to **18** before anyone sees what you have on!

59

Cromwell was to have two more battles in Britain. In 1649 he went to Ireland to put down a rebellion. He was harsh with the people. He killed many people who were not soldiers in the towns of Drogheda and Wexford. He said that this was because they did not give up the town. Many Irish people were killed in cold blood. Roman Catholic priests were singled out as well. He went on giving Irish land to the English. This ruthless treatment is part of the history of the Northern Ireland troubles today.

Cromwell also defeated the Scots in 1650. Charles I's son had been declared King of Great Britain, in Edinburgh. After the defeat Prince Charles escaped. The Commonwealth, as the rule without King was known, lasted from 1649 until 1660.

After a while Cromwell ruled on his own. He was known as the Lord Protector. This was partly because the Parliament did things like voting to keep their own seats without an election. They also said that no-one could vote unless Parliament thought that his opinions were such that he should be allowed to vote! Even if someone was elected, Parliament could rule that he was not the right sort of person to be in Parliament! During Cromwell's rule Puritan laws had to be obeyed. Theatres were shut. Cromwell died in 1658. Go to **60**.

60

Now, in 1660 the country is not being ruled well. You have become an adviser to one of the new Members of Parliament. You can advise him to let Parliament go on ruling – go to **110**, let the army rule – **95** or invite Prince Charles to come back as King – **7**.

61

St. Paul's does not look like the early churches, it was not built in the 'Gothic' style! Wren snorts in disgust. Lose 1 Life Point and go to **66**.

62

You feel the sting of shot as it snicks your arm. The shot has not stuck into you but it hurts like mad! Lose one Life Point and go to **40**.

63

You put butter on the sores. The butter is rancid (going bad) and does not help. In fact it seems to make it worse! Lose one Life Point and go to **53**.

64

Well done! You are east of Africa. You have found the route East. Add one Life Point to your score.

Vasco da Gama goes on to sail up the East African coast. Then he finds someone to show him the way to India. After two years, with half his men left, he returns to Portugal. He is a rich man.

For the next hundred years the Portuguese dominate trade to India, Malaysia, Japan and the Spice Islands. You bring back some cinnamon, nutmeg and cloves as a reminder of your sea trip! Write down *Spices* on your Equipment List.

Now you can go to join Christopher Columbus – **26**, John Cabot – **72** or back to Time Patrol Headquarters – **102**.

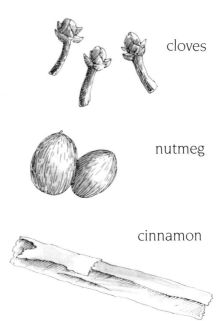

cloves

nutmeg

cinnamon

65

All over Europe there was conflict between the new Protestant ideas and the Roman Catholic Church. Christians from each side made life hard for the others. Catholic countries like Spain were cruel to Protestants. Protestant countries like Germany were cruel to Catholics. Sometimes they burnt people alive! They thought it would be better for the victims to suffer some pain in this life than pain for ever in the world beyond.

Now Mary Tudor, the daughter of Henry VIII and Catherine of Aragon, is on the throne. She is a Roman Catholic. She bans the use of the English Prayer Book and brings the Roman Catholic Church back to England. Now Thomas the Time Destroyer is in her court. He tells her to wipe out the Protestant movement in Britain. You can try and stop her being cruel to Protestants – go to **74** or try to get Thomas thrown out of court – go to **83**.

66

In the end Wren's Cathedral looked like this.

It is now famous and *was* based on the dome at St. Peter's church in Rome. You think that it is time you reported to Time Leader. Go to **100**.

67

You go to the Time Machine Bay. Do you have the Nexus Points, the Numeral Chart and the Event Chart? Check your Equipment List. Go and visit the Computer Room (**51**) and library (**23**) if you have not. If you have all three go to **68**.

68

You find that your Time Machine has been mended. The mechanic mutters something about bad Time driving as she walks off. You are ready to go. The first thing to check is the reign of Henry VII. Will you set the Time Controls to 1509 (go to **11**), 1485 (go to **94**) or 1702 (go to **34**)? You can check the dates on the Event Chart at **50**. (Don't forget to make a note of this number if you do!)

69

The sailor is a skilled fighter. The sword slashes past your face as you duck to one side. The wide blade makes a whooshing sound as it just misses you. You are being forced back as the sailor jumps and whirls. You do not have a weapon. You only have a leg of salt pork which you try to use as a club. You hold it up as the sailor brings his sword down for another blow. The sword sticks into the pork! As he tries to work the sword free you kick him in the leg. He falls to the ground. Then you see that all the Spanish have given up!

Drake loots the ship. It is the galleon *Cacafuego*. There is a great treasure on board. There are 360,000 Spanish gold coins (pieces of eight) and chests of gold, diamonds, silver and rubies!

The voyage goes on and Drake plunders other ships as well as making spice deals in Indonesia. You arrive back in England with 51 out of a crew of 160.

It is 1580. The voyage around the world has taken 3 years. Drake was the first Englishman to go around the world. Drake ended up with a great treasure. The amount was kept secret but was over £1,500,000! Queen Elizabeth had invested some money too. The Spanish are very angry with Drake but Queen Elizabeth met Drake and knighted him. You get your share too! Write down *Spanish Treasure* on your Equipment List. There was no sign of Thomas, but at least you are rich! Now go to **49** and look somewhere else.

70

SPANISH ARMADA PRINTOUT

Reasons for the Armada

- Philip was the head of many Catholics. Elizabeth was seen by some as leader of the Protestants. Philip felt it was his duty to humble England.

- England was helping the Dutch to rebel against Spain (Holland was also Protestant).

- The Spanish were fed up with the English taking their gold and plundering their ships.

- Elizabeth (against her will) had finally executed her cousin Mary, Queen of Scots, who had plotted with France to put a Roman Catholic back on the throne.

Why the Armada failed

- The English had faster and slimmer ships.

- The English had skilful captains fighting in their own waters.

- The weather was against the Spanish. A storm sank many of their galleons.

- The troops the Spanish hoped to pick up in Belgium never arrived.

Note: It is up to the Time Patrol to make sure that the Armada does fail. Make sure those things *do* happen.

Now go back to the place you were.

71

It is 1588. The Armada left Spain with 132 ships, 22,000 men and 180 priests. Elizabeth was to be burnt alive and the English were to be converted to the Roman Catholic Church. On 14th July a warship sees them. The warning fires are lit along the south coast. When the huge galleons come up the Channel they look like floating castles. (You will need to find out more at **70**.)

On July 19th, you are watching Drake (now Vice-Admiral) playing bowls on Plymouth Hoe. Captain Fleming, of the *Golden Hind* rushes up and tells Drake that the Spanish have been sighted. You remind Drake that the tide is running up the channel. The wind has slackened. The English ships cannot be moved out at the moment. Drake says that there is plenty of time to finish the game and thrash the Spaniards as well!

The Spanish ships stand high in the water. They roll in the rough water of the Channel. The wind blows the Armada up the Channel. The troop ships are in the middle of the galleons. The English ships follow. They twist in and out of range of the galleons. On the night of 22nd July the Armada is anchored off Calais. Will you advise that you attack with cannon – go to **28** or send fireships in – go to **77**.

72

After Columbus had found the West Indies, others thought there might be a way to the Spice Islands in a 'north-west passage'. That is, a way west, but to the north of what had already been found. This time Henry VII of England was one of the backers of another explorer. He was John Cabot (really John Cabotto, an Italian). He set sail in 1497 and you find a place as a *gromet*, a young person who was given lots of odd jobs around the ship.

You set sail. One day you are sorting out the food stores. You see a shadow in the dark hold. Someone is taking a powder out of a wooden box. He is about to pour it into the water stores! It is one of the Time Destroyers! He is going to kill the crew with poison. You rush up to him. Throw your dice and prepare to meet:

THE POISONER
FIGHTING SKILLS 7

As you grab him, he draws a dagger. He thrusts it at you and you leap to one side.

If you win go to **91**, if you lose go to **104**.

73

You take the ring with thanks. It has some letters on it. Write down *Signet Ring* on your Equipment List.

You get back into the
coach and complete
your trip into London.
You get out near an inn
called *The Dolphin*.
As you walk down the
narrow, cobbled street,
traders shout out their
wares. Eggs, cakes,
rabbits, and all kinds of
goods are being sold.
Basket-makers, tinkers
and other tradesmen
shout out too. It is
noisy, smelly and
crowded. An open gutter
runs down the middle of
the street. Horse and
carts compete for space
– manure is everywhere!
You duck as a bowl of
dirty water is thrown
into the street from an
upstairs room!

You step into the tavern. There are pots of food cooking over
an open fire and joints of meat and birds roasting on spits.
You can have some goose pie, stewed carp, buttered shrimp
or tanzy (eggs and cream). In the end you decide that roast
chicken would be safest!

You sit at a table. You get talking to a man sitting next to you.
He is full of gossip and stories. You find out that it is Samuel
Pepys. He kept a diary of the times that became famous. *The
Dolphin* is one of his favourite taverns. Pepys tells you that
the plague is starting in London. This is the same plague as
the Black Death of the 14th century. It is spread by the black
rat, which carries the fleas of the plague. The fleas bite and
the bacteria that give the plague are passed on. Very often
the black rats came to London in the holds of ships.

Over the next few weeks the plague gets worse. There was no known cure then. People who became ill were taken to a 'pest house'. This was little more than a shed where you lay until you died or got better. Only one person in three lived if they got the plague. The infected person's house was shut up for 40 days. On June 7th 1665 Pepys wrote in his diary:

'This day I did in Drury Lane see two or three houses marked with a red cross on the door and "Lord have Mercy upon us" writ there, which was a sad sight to me.'

Mass graves or 'plague pits' were dug. At one time 1000 people a day died; about 70,000 altogether died in London. At last, by December, the plague had died down. Cleaner streets and better water helped in later years. Also brown rats became more common. The black rat that carried the plague was driven out. Now go to **10**.

74

Mary has married Philip II, the King of Spain. You try and get him to tell Mary not to force Protestants back to the Roman Catholic Church. This is what Philip does, but Mary takes no notice. Go to **92**.

75

The sudden charge takes you by surprise. Thomas's rapier slashes your cheek. A thin line of blood appears. Lose one Life Point and throw again. If you win go to **43**. If you lose you are weak from loss of blood. Start this paragraph again if you are still alive!

You know what Henry did from History. You think that if you give an idea to one of Henry's advisers he might take notice. You wait until later in the evening. Many have been drinking. The King and his advisers wonder what to do about the Barons. As they are a little drunk they ask you, a servant, to give your ideas. They want to have some fun. Throw your dice and prepare to meet:

THE KING'S DRUNKEN ADVISER
FIGHTING SKILLS 8

If you win go to **88**, if you lose go to **115**.

Some old merchant ships are filled with bonfires and tar barrels. They are set alight and let go. They head into the Spanish ships that are still anchored close together. The fully loaded guns fire when the flames reach the gunpowder. The Spanish ships scatter. Some catch fire and one runs aground. When daylight comes the Spanish ships are scattered so the English ships move in. You are in one of the English ships. It is a fast ship with many guns. You see Drake in the *Revenge* and Lord Howard of Effingham in the flagship the *Ark Royal*. The Spanish ships have a high poop deck (at the stern or back of the ship) and forecastle (at the bow or front of the ship). They have many soldiers and they try to close, grapple and board.

You see one of the galleons trying to get close to your ship. You think you see Thomas the Time Destroyer on the ship, but you cannot be sure. Throw your dice and prepare to meet:

THE SPANISH GALLEON
FIGHTING SKILLS 20

If you win go to **113**. If you lose go to **109**.

78

You decide that the best place to be is at Henry's court. Henry VIII came to the throne in 1509. He was a fine horseman and spoke French, Latin and Spanish (as well as English!). You will have to dress in the correct way if you are to go to Henry's court.

You go to the Time Patrol's clothing store. You can be a Tudor nobleman (go to **79**) or noblewoman (go to **80**).

79

You will go as a Nobleman. You wear a short velvet cloak, lined with fur. A 'doublet' (a tight-fitting tunic) is worn over a silk shirt. There are layers of rich patterned linings. Open shoes are worn over stockings with short breeches. Now go to **81**.

80

You will go as a
Noblewoman. You wear
a dress of heavy velvet.
It is sewn with silver
thread in many patterns.
Large sleeves are
worn with coloured
petticoats. Jewels are
sewn into your hat
·and you wear a gold
necklace and belt.
Now go to **81**.

81

You set the Time Machine controls to arrive in England in
1532. One evening you go to Henry's court. The Tudors liked
to eat well. Breakfast was only a snack, but the main meal
was huge. The 'rere supper' in the evening was a banquet in
the houses of the rich and most people ate a lot of meat
(not many vegetables!).

Henry VIII is having a feast this evening. (He liked his food!)
There are oxen and pigs roasting on long spits over an open
fire. Some of the new spices from the East – pepper, cloves
and ginger – are being used to flavour the meat. Honey is
also used and is poured over the meat.

Many people are dressed in fancy costumes and masks. There is music playing. You find yourself humming a song. It is a well-known tune called 'Greensleeves'. Just then Henry himself passes you! He hears your tune. He looks at you. He tells you to hum the tune again. He goes off thinking hard. Some say that 'Green Sleaves', as it was known then, was written by Henry VIII himself. Perhaps he got the idea from you! You think that you had better not tell Time Leader about this. It is too strange. He writes a song – you hear it in the future – then you go back and hum it – he hears it and writes it – you hear it in the future ...! It couldn't have happened like that – could it?

Well, at least you have got an invitation to join Henry at his top table.

Henry is rather happy about his reign so far. He began thinking of himself as a warrior king. He won an important battle against the Scots (defeating and killing James IV of Scotland at Flodden). He also put on a good display when meeting the French King at the so called Cloth of Gold in France. Here the two Kings spent a great deal of money to impress each other. The war with France was not settled however. Now Henry is trying to divorce his wife, Catherine of Aragon.

You find yourself sitting next to the Archbishop of Canterbury, Thomas Cranmer. You hope he will explain things to you. At the moment he shows no interest in you. You can tell him about your sea trips – **55** or try and interest him in some new kind of wine – **98**.

82

You go back to your Time Machine. You do not know where to go yet! Also, the Time Machine has not been mended. Lose 1 Life Point for wasting time and choose the Computer at **51** or the library at **23**.

You say that Thomas is a traitor. He has been there longer than you. They think that *you* are the traitor. You have to leave! Go to **92**.

84

You wear loose trousers fastened to your coat. The trousers, or breeches end below the knee and are tied with ribbon. You wear wide leather boots. A plumed hat sits atop your long curly hair (a wig!). You also keep the sword you had from when you fought in the Civil War. Now go to **57**.

85

You wear a high-waisted skirt of satin. The fine petticoats are shown and you wear lace at cuff and collar. Pearls complete the outfit. You also keep the sword you had from when you fought in the Civil War safe in the Time Machine. Now go to **57**.

86

You rush up to the robbers. One of them turns and hits you over the head with a club. You are stunned for a moment. Lose one Life Point. Now throw your dice again. If you win, go to **111**. If you lose, go to the beginning of this paragraph again.

87

You move to one side and the sword slashes past you. Then the sailor's boot thumps into your side. Lose one Life Point as you try to catch your breath. Then throw your dice again. If you win go to **69**. If you lose start this paragraph again!

88

You tell the adviser that there should be a place where the nobles can be given a trial before the Law. Henry has made judges to go around the land, but they are afraid of the nobles. The adviser pretends that he does not think much of the idea. Yet the next week Henry starts his Star Chamber. This was a court under the Privy Council, under Henry's control. The Barons were tamed and the power of the throne was created.

Henry's reign was important for the start of new learning, but also for the start of many explorations and discoveries. This is one of the Nexus Points of this era. You find that this is what the Time Destroyers are planning to change. You follow Thomas Wright (or Nardek). He drops a piece of paper. You pick it up. It is a map of important explorations. Write *Map of Sea Travels* on your Equipment List. You can see this at **89**.

Now you will have to take to the sea as an adventurer or 'sea-dog'! Go to **89**.

Trade was becoming more and more important. People went overland a long way to trade for gold, silks, spices and jewels. They went overland to the Middle and Far East, often by camel train. This took a long time and the Turks made it difficult sometimes. Your Map of Sea Travels will make this clear.

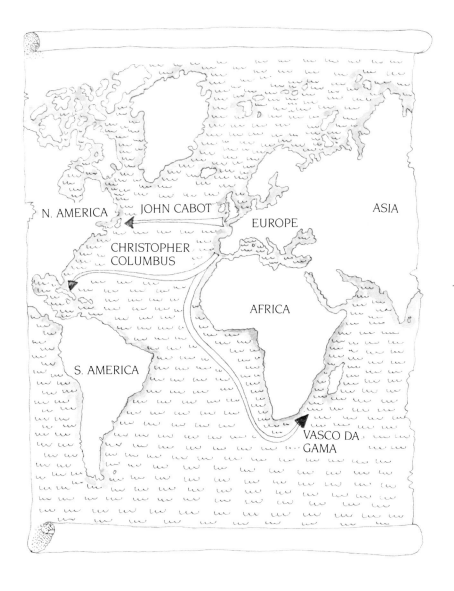

People wanted a quicker way to the 'Spice' of the East. Some said a western sea route would be best. Others said that south was best. When these routes were found the Western countries discovered a lot more of the World! The Time Destroyers think that if they can stop these discoveries they can change History. You must make sure the voyages go as planned.

You can go to sea with Christopher Columbus – go to **26**, Vasco da Gama – go to **42** or John Cabot – go to **72**.

90

The manor house is very grand. It is to be made in the well-known 'E' plan. This was an entrance porch, a large hall and two wings with kitchens and living rooms. A new building material is being used. It is red brick made from clay. The top floor has a long gallery running the whole length of the house. Here people would walk, children would play or music and dancing would take place.

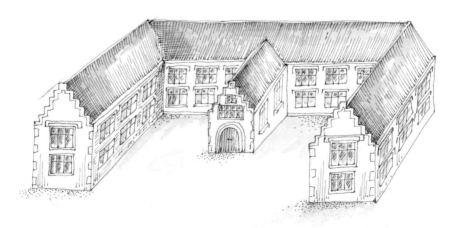

The builder is thinking hard about the chimneys. He shows you the drawings. You can tell him to put a gas fire in – go to **119**, make some long chimneys with a wide fireplace – go to **101** or leave a hole in the roof – go to **33**.

91

The dagger misses you. It stabs one of the wooden water barrels. As the poisoner tries to get the knife out you push him to the floor. You call for help. Some other sailors come in. You show them the poison. You tell the bosun (in charge of the running of the ship) that the poisoner must be a spy. He accepts this and the poisoner is locked up.

You are told to get on deck and start sounding the water depth. You take a 'lead-line' from the stores. You drop it over the side and reel out the line to see how deep the water is. The seabed appears to be getting shallower. Then you see a flight of birds!

John Cabot has not found the West Indies or the Spice Islands. He *has* found a large island off the eastern Canadian coast. He calls it Newfoundland. The first British colony will be founded there. This led to a good trade in fish. You fish for a cod which you keep to remind you. Write down *Cod* on your Equipment List.

Now you can go to join Vasco da Gama – **42**, Christopher Columbus – **26** or go back to the Time Patrol Headquarters – **102**.

Mary burnt over 300
people in her reign.
She became known as
'Bloody Mary'. (Even so,
others also burned
people for their
religion.) She burnt
Archbishop Cranmer as
well as other Bishops
like Latimer and Ridley.
When he was burnt,
Ridley said 'We shall
light such a candle as
shall never be put out'.
He was right because
Britain became
Protestant in the end
(but not before a lot
more cruelty and
argument).

You are sorry that you could not stop the burning. Once
again History seems to have a pace of its own. These things
did happen. Now you find that Thomas the Time Destroyer
has gone again. As you think on these things you go back to
your Time Machine. There is a message. It is a call for help.
A fellow Time Patroller is in trouble! You look at the date –
1563! You set the time and go! Go to **97**.

93

You go into London Town and see if you can find Thomas.
After an hour of walking you come to some building work.
You see that a big manor house is being built, as well as
some smaller town houses. The smaller houses are being
built on a wooden framework. Oak beams are being used.

You spend some time helping the carpenters cut trunks into planks. The spaces between the oak frames will be filled with whitewashed plaster panels. This gives the black and white look to Tudor houses.

You talk to the *sawyers* (the men who are sawing the tree-trunks). They do not seem to have seen Thomas. You go over to the men working on the manor house, about half a mile away. Go to **90**.

94

Well done! You checked the date well. You are all set to go to 1485, the start of the Tudors and when Henry the Seventh (VII) came to the throne.

You set the Time Controls. There is a hum and a smell of burning. Everything goes black around you. Then you see a grey mist flow past you like fog. All at once you land with a bump. You are in the year 1485.

The Wars of the Roses are over. Henry Tudor, head of the House of Lancaster (Red Rose) has married Princess Elizabeth of the House of York (White Rose). You go to the court of Henry VII to see what the Barons are up to. You will wear a rose emblem on your tunic. Which rose will you wear? Which rose will the new House of Tudor choose for its emblem? If you think the White Rose go to **107**, the Red Rose go to **58** or something else go to **18**.

The army did take over for a while, but not for long. Go back to **60** and choose again.

96

The highwayman or 'tobyman' has chosen his spot carefully. He has a drawn pistol and he rides up alongside the coach. He tells the driver to stop. You are all made to get out.

Sometimes highwaymen were well-known people locally. Some (not all!) had a sense of humour. You wonder if he will take a chance with you. People often had duels in those days. You say that you will fight him. If he wins you will hand over your goods without any trouble. If you win he must let you go. He agrees.

Throw your dice and prepare to meet:

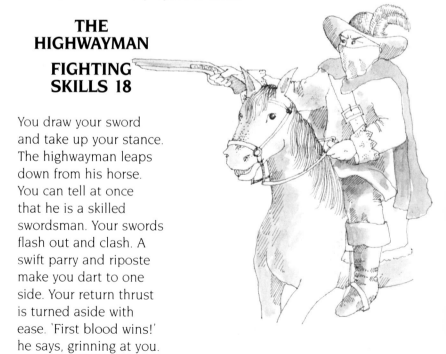

THE
HIGHWAYMAN

FIGHTING
SKILLS 18

You draw your sword and take up your stance. The highwayman leaps down from his horse. You can tell at once that he is a skilled swordsman. Your swords flash out and clash. A swift parry and riposte make you dart to one side. Your return thrust is turned aside with ease. 'First blood wins!' he says, grinning at you.

If you win go to **4**, if you lose go to **114**.

97

You arrive to find Mark, a Time Patroller, being set upon by vagabonds. They are robbers roaming the country. Many people are poor. This is because many of the rich had fenced in common land for their own use (called enclosures). Also more sheep were kept meaning fewer jobs for farm workers. Monasteries, which had helped care for the poor, had been closed (by Henry VIII) and many people were homeless.

You go to help Mark. Throw your dice and prepare to meet:

ELIZABETHAN VAGABOND
FIGHTING SKILLS 7

If you win go to **111**, if you lose go to **86**.

98

Check your Equipment List. Do you have any spices? If you do, read on, if not you will need to go back to **89** and go on a sea voyage!

You find that you have some cinnamon and cloves. You take some red wine. You stir in some ground cinnamon. Then you add some cloves. Finally you thrust a hot poker from the fire into the wine. You have made mulled wine! Thomas Cranmer thinks it is very tasty! The wine relaxes him.

Cranmer tells you that Catherine of Aragon, Henry's wife, had been married to Henry's brother, Arthur. When Arthur died, the Pope, the Head of the Roman Catholic Church, had said Henry could marry his brother's widow. Catherine had six children. All died except one, Mary. Henry wanted a male heir as it was thought a woman ruler could not reign. (How wrong they were!) Now he wanted to marry a woman of the court, Anne Boleyn. The Pope would not let Henry divorce Catherine as it was against Roman Catholic law. (Henry was claiming that the marriage was not valid as he had married his brother's widow.) The Pope was also a prisoner of Emperor Charles V of Spain. As Catherine was Spanish, Charles V did not want her disgraced by being divorced.

Your head reels under all these facts. You can hardly make any sense of it. It is like a maze! All this trouble over rules made in Rome, says Cranmer. The rulers of Catholic countries were subject to the Pope in those times. You tell him that as Henry is a strong King why doesn't he just decide himself. He could start his own Church with himself as Head. Cranmer stares at you. It is a simple idea, but it could work he says. He jumps up and can be seen talking quickly to Henry.

Just then you see Thomas Wright, the Time Destroyer. He is hurrying out of the door. You decide to follow him. Go to **99**.

99

You run after the Time Destroyer. Suddenly Thomas Wright turns and faces you. He is holding one of the early guns! It is a musket. He props it up on a long stick and takes aim! Throw your dice and prepare to meet:

THOMAS: THE TUDOR MUSKETEER
FIGHTING SKILLS 12

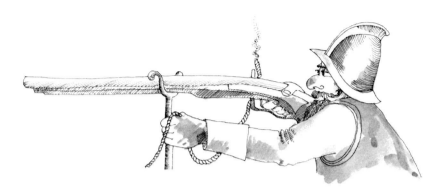

The gun goes off with a flash of gunpowder. In these matchlock guns a lighted match is lowered into a pan of gunpowder. A great cloud of white smoke goes up. You cannot see Thomas.

If you win go to **39**, if you lose go to **62**.

100

Time Leader is pleased with your work so far. She says that the Civil War, the Protectorate and the Restoration have gone as they should have. She goes on, 'I do not think it was Thomas who set fire to the baker's shop. Even if it was he made a mistake. The Great Fire *did* happen. Once again you, as a Time Patroller, must stand by and let History take its course. You cannot stop all the suffering and pain. But again you seem unable to stop giving ideas to people on building. You've got it right so far, but be careful!'

Time Leader then tells you that you must go on to the last Nexus Points of the period. The Bill of Rights and other Acts of Parliament may not be very exciting, but they are very important for the future, she says. After a day or two of rest you dress in the clothes of a 'courtier' (someone who was at the King or Queen's court). You take these clothes from the Time Patrol wardrobe. Then you set the Time to 1689.
Go to **21**.

101

Coal was being used in those days. Coal produces a nastier smoke than wood. Also having a chimney flue meant that you could build extra floors instead of just one big hall with a hole in the roof. The Tudors used long, fancy chimneys. You sketch out a fireplace and chimney layout for the builder.

The master builder, a man of some importance, is pleased. He gives you a card. It is an invitation to attend Queen Elizabeth's court for a public event. Write down *Court Invitation* on your Equipment List.

Now go back to **49** and choose again.

102

You go back to the Time Patrol Headquarters. Have you been to the main explorers of this time? You should have been with Vasco da Gama (42), Christopher Columbus (26) and John Cabot (72). You should have Spices, Coconut and Cod on your Equipment List. Check! If you do not go back to **42**, **26** or **72**! If you have them all, read on.

You arrive back at Time Patrol Headquarters. You go and report to Time Leader. She is pleased. You have made sure that important places have been found. History shows that the Americas were found at around this time. So was the route around Africa. Add two Life Points to your score. Time Leader is not happy that you tried to tell Columbus that he was wrong. 'In History Columbus thought to the day he died that he had found a western route to the Spice Islands.

What if he had taken notice of what you said? Then the West Indies would be called something else. A small point perhaps. But who knows how History might have been changed after that.'

Just as you turn to go, Time Leader asks you what that smell is. You tell her it is a fish! She is very unhappy about you taking things from the past. She feels better when you make her a meal of the fish (cod) cooked in a coconut sauce! But that does not stop her sending you back into History. It is all work, work, work you think to yourself.

There will be more explorations and discoveries later, but now you have to visit the time of King Henry VIII. Go to **78**.

103

The Time Leader is quite pleased with you. You did not find Thomas, but you have stopped most of his mischief so far. The great expeditions and discoveries of the period have gone ahead. It is a pity that Time Leader takes all your Spanish treasure away! She says it belongs to Time Patrol! Oh well, at least she did not go on about your advice to the master builder this time, you think to yourself.

Also you made sure the Spanish Armada was stopped. The Time Destroyers were trying to help Spain at this time. They gave wrong advice, but you gave good advice! Add three Life Points to your score. Just as you decide that it is time to have a holiday Time Leader tells you that you have to go to the Stuart period. There is a plot to blow up King James!
Go to **126**.

104

As you jump away, you push his arm. Some of the powder falls into one of the water barrels. Lose one Life Point as this will make the rest of the trip very thirsty! Throw your dice and try again as he comes at you. (Go back to bottom of **72**.)

105

Cromwell's troops are not ready. The Royalists capture Bristol. Go and train at **24**.

106

You draw up a list of reforms. These are:

People must be given a reason for being arrested and not just locked up without trial. (This became the Habeas Corpus Act.)

The Queen or King could not rule or make taxes without Parliament. They also could not keep their own army in time of peace. (The rule that no ruler could be a Roman Catholic was added and these ideas became the Bill of Rights.)

Now go to **38** and choose again.

107

You put on a White Rose. Quickly you see that you have made a mistake. Go to **18** before anyone sees what you have on!

108

You tell John Churchill that the French are becoming a strong force in Europe. You say that he is the man to stop them. You say he will be famous and rich. He stays with William and Mary. Later, in the reign of Queen Anne he had some famous victories. One was Blenheim in 1704. Churchill became the Duke of Marlborough. Blenheim Palace was built for him. Now go back to **38** and choose again.

109

The galleon's cannons fire. One of the cannonballs crashes into the rigging of your ship. Lose one Life Point and throw again. If you lose, read this paragraph again. If you win, go to **113**.

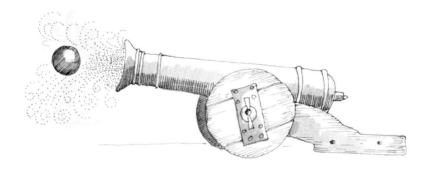

110

The men who had been in government 19 years before were recalled. The army disbanded them. Parliament did not rule alone. Go to **60** and choose again.

111

One of the robbers tries to hit you with a club made from a tree branch. You duck and push him over. He falls in the mud. The robbers then all run off. Two are very thin and weak. They do not want a fight. The third man was a Time Destroyer. He had a knife and you see that Mark is wounded. Blood drips down his sleeve.

Just then some soldiers come up. The Time Destroyer has told them that *you* are the thief! You are still wearing clothes from Henry VIII's time. They are old and dirty. You look like a vagabond (a person with no home). Mark rides off but you are taken off to a judge. Go to **112**.

Here are some of the punishments you might be given:

Boiled or burnt alive (mostly for murderers)
Ears cut off and nose slit open (for robbers)
Hands cut off (sheep stealers)
Whipped or put in stocks (vagabonds)
Ducked in water on ducking stool
Put in pillory
Branded with red-hot iron

The Time Destroyer, who is dressed as a farmer, claims that you are a cutpurse. (In those days purses were tied to a belt by a leather strap. A cutpurse would cut the strap and take the purse.)

As no one else is there to agree with him the judge gives you a lesser punishment. First you are ducked in water and then put in the pillory.

While you are in the pillory you get rotten fruit thrown at you. When evening comes Mark arrives. He has had his wound seen to at Time Patrol. Now he lets you out. He also laughs at your smell and discomfort. You do not think it funny. You think it even less funny when he tells you that you will have to do his work.

You have to look all over the Elizabethan Time for Thomas the Time Destroyer who is up to mischief. You tell him that he will have to look after himself next time!

The first thing you need to do is get a bath and some new clothes. You go back to your Time Machine and visit Time Patrol Headquarters. Time Leader turns up her nose when you get there. You glare at her and go for your bath.

After you are clean you think about what clothes to wear. You think that a rich person's clothes will help you get to more places. You can choose to be an Elizabethan Gentleman (go to **36**) or an Elizabethan Lady (go to **37**).

113

The galleon fires. Its crew is not as well-trained as yours. The cannonballs pass by and splash in the water. Your ship twists and turns. You help the gunners fire volley after volley into the Spanish galleon. The cannons get red-hot as they fire. The cannon recoils after each firing and it has to be reloaded. It is hot and dangerous work. At last you hole the galleon below deck and it starts to sink! The English fleet keeps on at the Armada. It uses long-range cannon fire as the main tactic.

The next day the wind changes. The Armada is driven out to the
North Sea by strong winds. The English follow as far north as
Scotland. Many ships run out of powder and cannonballs!
They give up the chase. The damaged Armada now has to go
all around north Scotland and to the west of Ireland to get
home. Fierce storms arise. The gales wreck many of the ships.

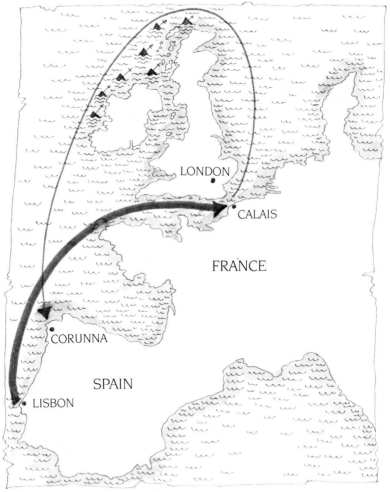

130 ships set sail. Only 53 returned. England lost less men
(60) than the Armada lost ships! It was a great victory. Later,
in James I's reign, peace was made with Spain.

You have helped stop the Armada! You think it is time to go back and report to Time Patrol Headquarters. Go to **103**.

114

You leap at him, blade forward. He moves to one side. As you go past, he kicks you. Then his sword grazes your hand. A drop of blood shows that he is the winner. Lose 2 Life Points.

The highwayman makes you hand over all your goods. When he rides off, one of your fellow travellers comes over to you. It is a woman, with many veils over her face. 'You tried!' she says. 'Here, I have hidden this ring. Take it!' Now go to **73**.

115

The adviser just laughs at you. He pushes you away and tells you that you are a fool. Lose 1 Life Point and try again at **76**.

116

It is time to deal with Thomas the Time Destroyer! You have become quite good with the sword by now. You have learnt at Time Headquarters and had some practice on your travels. You ask Thomas to fight a duel. They were common in those days. You take up your position with a rapier and a dagger. The rapier was a thin, thrusting sword with a short grip. The dagger was a 'parrying' dagger for fending off or parrying the other person's sword. It was sometimes called a *main gauche* from the French meaning 'left hand'.

Throw your dice and prepare to meet:

THOMAS THE SWORDSMAN
FIGHTING SKILLS 20

You are both skilled. The battle rages back and forth. You
parry a thrust and twist at his sword with your dagger.
He frees his sword and lunges under your dagger.

If you lose go to **123**, if you win go to **125**.

117

Check your Equipment List. Do you have the Elizabethan
Dance Steps, the Spanish Treasure and the Court Invitation?
Only go on if you have all three. If you do not go back to **49**
and choose again. Go to **118** if you have them all.

118

You hire a horse at a local inn. You ride out to Hampton
Court where Elizabeth I was holding court that day. When you
arrive, you are asked for your invitation.

You are let into the ballroom. Queen Elizabeth and her courtiers are dancing. You will have to join in. Check your Equipment List. If you have the Elizabethan Dance Steps you may read on. If not you will need to go to the theatre and learn them (**8**).

You dance a *Pavane* first. This is slow and solemn. There is a lot of bowing and pointing of the leg. Then the music gets faster and faster. You dance a *Jig*, then a leaping, twisting dance called the *Lavolta*.

At last, puffed out, you sit down to rest. You see Sir Francis Drake talking to the Queen. You also see Thomas there! He is talking to them. You must find out what is being said! Check your Equipment List. Do you have the Spanish Treasure? If you do read on. (If you do not you must go back to **22** and join the *Golden Hind*.)

You go up to Drake. He turns to the Queen. He tells her that you are one of his (now rich!) crew. The Queen has been talking about King Philip II of Spain. He is King of a powerful and rich Empire. From time to time Elizabeth has thought about marrying him. She kept changing her mind. She wanted to stop Philip making war on England. Now Thomas is urging Elizabeth to marry Philip II. What will you advise? If you tell Elizabeth to marry Philip go to **5**. If you think she should not, go to **127**.

119

What? They did not have gas in those days. The fuel was wood or coal. Lose one Life Point and choose long chimneys – **101** or a hole in the roof – **33**.

120

Charles did not ask Parliament. When he agreed with them he often broke his promise. Lose one Life Point and go to **124**.

121

Thomas shakes off your grasp. He hits you in the face with a bit of rope. The rope slices into you and you flinch. Lose one Life Point and throw your dice again. Go to **13** if you win or start again at this paragraph if you lose..

122

You decide to be a Royalist. This could change History if your help allows Charles to become a dictator. Choose again at **124**.

123

Lose 2 Life Points as Thomas cuts your arm. Throw your dice and try again. Go to **125** if you win. Read this paragraph again if you lose and are still alive!

124

This is what happened:

1. When he ruled without Parliament Charles ran out of money. Charles's adviser, Buckingham, was killed. Later his adviser Stafford was voted a traitor by Parliament. (Charles had called Parliament to raise money.)

2.. He did not get them to agree on taxes, breaking the Petition of Rights which said he must do so.

3. Charles raised the Ship Money for the Navy by taxing all the land. Because this was not agreed by Parliament some, like John Hampden, would not pay.

4. In 1642 Charles marched into the House of Commons with armed guards. He wanted to arrest five Members of Parliament. People were angry. No King had done this before.

5. He did not agree to what Parliament asked, yet wanted money to rule.

Civil War will be fought between the Royalists (for the King) and the Parliamentarians (for Parliament). You will have to choose the winning side. You may like to check the Event Chart at **50**. You can be a Royalist – go to **122** or a Parliamentarian – go to **19**.

125

You catch Thomas's sword and dagger on yours. You push hard and he is thrown to the floor. You are made the winner by the judge. Then, to your surprise, Thomas takes out one of the new (for this age) flintlock pistols. He fully cocks the pistol and fires. 'Die, Time Patrol!' he shouts as the gunpowder is set off and the ball flies at you. You are hit in the arm and Thomas runs off. He is never seen again! The pistol shot has passed out of your arm. You tie up the wound with a clean, lace handkerchief. Now go to **38** and choose again.

It is the year 1605. James I of England has been on the throne for two years. He was the son of Mary Stuart and has been King James VI of Scotland since he was two years old. He was the first Stuart ruler of England.

You are in a dark cellar under the Houses of Parliament. You hear some whispering from the next cellar. The light of a lantern flashes. You look into the room through a crack in the door. You see some men. They are stacking firewood and gunpowder in the cellar. Thomas the Time Destroyer is there too! The plan is to blow up the Houses of Parliament when James I is there. A group of Roman Catholics have planned this. They had hoped that James would make the country Roman Catholic again. James was the son of Mary, Queen of Scots, who was Catholic. Now they want to kill him as he did not want to change the religion.

You report the men to the guards. The Roman Catholic soldier who was stacking the gunpowder, Guy Fawkes, is arrested. (Thomas escapes.) The other plotters are also arrested. They were executed as traitors. Nowadays Bonfire Night, when a 'Guy' is burnt, is a reminder of this event. At first the Protestant rulers of England wanted people to think of Catholics as plotters against the State. Now, of course, it is just a day for fireworks and fun. As you return to your Time Machine you think about the problems of religion in those times. James I was also under pressure from Protestants. One extreme group, the Puritans, were asking him for help. He did not agree. (He did order a translation of the Bible. This English version, the King James' Bible was used for many years afterwards.) Thomas may well be stirring things up with the Puritans, so you decide to check up on this. You decide to visit one of the Puritan groups. You can be a Puritan Man, or a Puritan Woman – go to **12**.

127

You tell the Queen not to marry Philip. This is what she plans anyway. Thomas is very angry. He mutters that he will go to the Spanish now. You follow him as he leaves. Once again you chase after him. He goes out into the gardens. The Tudor gardens were well-planned. They had trim paths with flower-beds in fancy shapes. Herbs and shrubs were carefully laid out. Sometimes a maze was planted. In fact, at Hampton Court there is a well-known maze. Thomas plunges into this and you lose him again. You decide that you had better stop all this running around and deal with the Nexus Point – the Spanish Armada. You go back to your Time Machine and print out the Spanish Armada file from the portable Computer. You can look at this at **70** when you wish. (Make a note of the number you're on.) Write down *Spanish Armada Printout* on your Equipment List. Then go to **71**.

128

You can only go back to Time Patrol if you have made a list of reforms at **106**, seen John Churchill at **108** or dealt with Thomas at **116**. If you have not you should go to these numbers now (or choose at **38**).

If you have been to these numbers you can go to **130**.

129

You tell Wren that the dome of St. Peter's Church in Rome is rather fine. He looks interested. Add 1 Life Point to your score and go to **66**.

130

Knowing how bad the treatment of wounds is in this age, you go back to Time Patrol Headquarters at once! You do not want your arm cut off because it goes bad!

As your arm is being treated at Time Patrol Headquarters, Time Leader comes in. 'You can have a holiday now,' she says. 'Queen Anne, the last of the Stuarts will now reign. The Act of Union between England and Scotland will be made in 1707. You have done well! History is kept as it should be. I may even think about giving you a rise in wages!'

This is the end of ROSES AND CAVALIERS. If you want more History adventures, look out for other books in the Time Patrol Series!

THE ROSES AND CAVALIERS ADVENTURE SHEET

Name ....

Each time you fight you must work out your Fighting Skill points.

You have already been given some Fighting Skill points for each fight.	+	Throw both your dice and write down the total number you have thrown.	=	Add your numbers together to find your total Fighting Skill points.

Skills points given   +   Dice throw   =   Your total Fighting Skill points

You win if you have the same or more Fighting Skill points than your enemy.

You lose if you have fewer Fighting Skill points than your enemy.

Enemy	Your Skill points	Dice throw	Your total Fighting Skill points	Enemy's Fighting Skill points	Win/Lose
King's Drunken Adviser	5 +		=		
Thomas: The Mad Sailor	5 +		=		
The Poisoner	4 +		=		
Thomas: The Tudor Musketeer	7 +		=		
Elizabethan Vagabond	4 +		=		
Spanish Sailor	9 +		=		
The Spanish Galleon	15 +		=		
Thomas: The Stuart Cavalier	11 +		=		
The Highwayman	13 +		=		
Thomas: The Swordsman	15 +		=		

Life Points	Equipment List	Story Number
25		